Fiddler's ten easy tunes for violin with piano accompaniment

MICHAEL ROSE

NOVELLO PUBLISHING LIMITED
8/9 Frith Street, London W1V 5TZ

Order No: NOV 192032

9.95

one Reverie *page* 1

two March 2

three Valse 4

four Song 7

five Pony ride 8

six On the swing 11

seven Gay dance 14

eight Sad story 16

nine Hide and seek 20

ten The old castle 25

These pieces were written to provide varied material for a pupil progressing from approximately Grade 1 to Grade 3 standard. Each piece introduces new elements, e.g. new finger/key patterns, new bowing considerations, new rhythmic patterns, and so on.

Bowings marked are only suggestions, and although all pieces are playable in first position, the judicious use of other positions may help to make their performance more effective.

Extra violin parts are available.

FIDDLER'S TEN

Easy tunes for violin
with piano accompaniment

MICHAEL ROSE

1 REVERIE

20197

2 MARCH

4

3 VALSE

poco rall.   a tempo

6

4 SONG

*slur optional

5 PONY RIDE

6 ON THE SWING

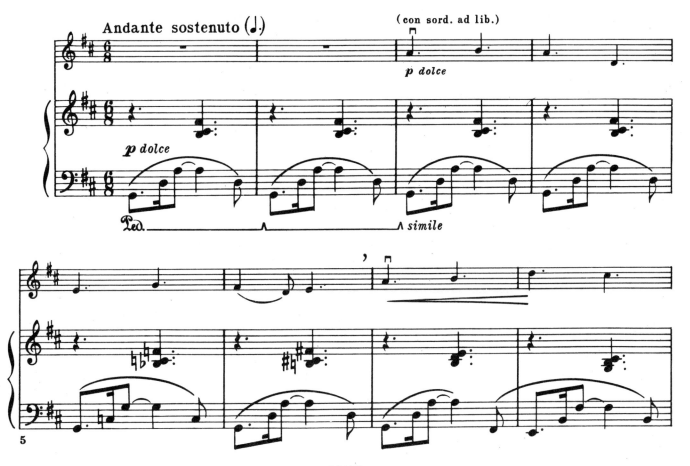

14

7 GAY DANCE

8 SAD STORY

poco rall. a tempo

cantabile

9 HIDE AND SEEK

10 THE OLD CASTLE

Printed in Great Britain by Headway Press Ltd

9/94 (18757)

STRING MUSIC FOR THE STUDENT

VIOLIN

COHEN, Eta
VIOLIN METHOD
Book 1
Book 2
Book 3

BENNETT, Richard Rodney
UP BOW, DOWN BOW (violin)

JACOBY, Robert
VIOLIN TECHNIQUE

ROSE, Michael
FIDDLER'S TEN

STONE, David
EIGHT PIECES IN THE THIRD
POSITION

SCALES AND ARPEGGIOS

VIOLA

BENNETT, Richard Rodney
UP BOW, DOWN BOW (viola)

BOLITHO, Una
TEN CAROLS

MILNE, Alison
PLAYING THE VIOLA

SCALES AND ARPEGGIOS

CELLO

BENOY AND BURROWES
CELLO METHOD
First Year
Second Year
Third Year

BURROWES *arr*
SIX EASY PIECES
Solo or duet

COLE AND SHUTTLEWORTH
PLAYING THE CELLO (tutor)

EVANS
CELLO TIME

EISENBERG, Maurice
CELLO PLAYING OF TODAY (tutor)

SCALES AND ARPEGGIOS

DOUBLE BASS

EVANS, Colin
BASIC BASS (open strings only)

612 (90)